ACHIEVE

The higher score

Year
6

Grammar, Spelling and Punctuation

SATs Question Workbook

Marie Lallaway & Madeleine Barnes

RISING STARS

Hachette UK's policy is to use papers that are natural, renewable and recyclable products and made from wood grown in sustainable forests. The logging and manufacturing processes are expected to conform to the environmental regulations of the country of origin.

Orders: please contact Bookpoint Ltd, 130 Park Drive, Milton Park, Abingdon, Oxon OX14 4SE. Telephone: (44) 01235 400555. Email: primary@bookpoint.co.uk.

Lines are open from 9 a.m. to 5 p.m., Monday to Saturday, with a 24-hour message answering service. Visit our website at www.risingstars-uk.com for details of the full range of Rising Stars publications.

Online support and queries email: onlinesupport@risingstars-uk.com

ISBN: 978 1 51044 288 7

© Rising Stars UK Ltd 2018
This edition published in 2018 by Rising Stars UK Ltd
First published in 2015 by Rising Stars UK Ltd
Rising Stars UK Ltd, part of Hodder Education Group
An Hachette UK Company
Carmelite House
50 Victoria Embankment
London EC4Y 0DZ

www.risingstars-uk.com

Impression number 10 9 8 7 6 5 4 3 2 1

Year 2022 2021 2020 2019 2018

Authors: Marie Lallaway and Madeleine Barnes

Series Editor: Madeleine Barnes

Accessibility Reviewer: Vivien Kilburn

Educational Adviser: Josh Lury

Cover design: Burville-Riley Partnership

Typeset in India

Printed in Slovenia

A catalogue record for this title is available from the British Library.

Contents

Welcome to Achieve GPS: The Higher Score – Question Workbook

In this book you will find lots of practice and information to help you achieve the higher score in the Key Stage 2 English Grammar, Punctuation and Spelling (GPS) tests. You will look again at some of the key knowledge that was in *Achieve the Expected Standard – Question Workbook,* but you will use it to tackle trickier questions and apply it in more complex ways.

About the Key Stage 2 Grammar, Punctuation and Spelling National Tests

The tests will take place in the summer term in Year 6. They will be done in your school and will be marked by examiners – not by your teacher.

The tests are divided into two papers:

Paper 1: questions – 45 minutes (50 marks)

- You will answer short questions about grammar, punctuation and language strategies.
- Some questions will ask you to tick a box, circle or underline. Other questions will ask you to add words to a sentence, or to rewrite it making a change. You may be asked to explain why a sentence is written in a particular way.
- The questions will include the language of grammar and punctuation.
- Most questions are worth 1 mark, but you should check to make sure before you answer each question in case you need to give more than one answer.
- Spelling counts for questions that test tenses, plurals, suffixes and contractions.

Paper 2: spelling – approximately 15 minutes (20 marks)

- Twenty sentences will be read aloud to you, one at a time. You will be asked to spell a particular word in each sentence.
- The words may be taken from the word lists for Years 1–6.
- Each correct answer is worth 1 mark.

Test techniques

Before the tests
- Try to revise little and often, rather than in long sessions.
- Choose a time of day when you are not tired or hungry.
- Choose somewhere quiet so you can focus.
- Revise with a friend. You can encourage and learn from each other.
- Read the 'Top tips' throughout this book to remind you of important points in answering test questions.
- Keep track of your score using the table on the inside back cover of this book.

During the tests
- READ THE QUESTION AND READ IT AGAIN.
- If you find a question difficult to answer, move on; you can always come back to it later.
- Always answer a multiple-choice question. If you really can't work out an answer, read the question again and try to think of the most sensible response.
- Check to see how many marks a question is worth. Have you written enough to 'earn' those marks in your answer?
- Read the question again after you have answered it. Make sure you have given the correct number of answers within a question, e.g. 'Tick **two**'.
- If you have any time left at the end, go back to the questions you have missed.

Where to get help:

- **Pages 6–23** practise grammar.
- **Pages 24–29** practise punctuation.
- **Pages 30–42** practise spelling. (Note that in the test the words for you to spell will be read to you in a sentence. These pages cannot replicate that format, so instead they allow you to practise spelling lots of common words that might appear in the test.)
- **Pages 45–48** provide the answers to the questions.

Nouns

To achieve the higher score, you need to know what nouns are and how to use them.

1 Write a sentence that uses the word <u>rush</u> as a **noun**. Remember to punctuate your answer correctly.

1

(1 mark)

2 Tick two boxes to show which sentences below contain **nouns**.

Tick **two**.

We have a strict bedtime routine. ☐

Can you give it to me later, please? ☐

She really likes you. ☐

Your rudeness is becoming a problem. ☐

2

(1 mark)

3 Rewrite the sentence below, changing the **noun** for another that makes sense. Remember to punctuate your answer correctly.

I understand your confusion.

3

(1 mark)

4 Underline the **nouns** in the sentence below.

The poem described a range of feelings such as love and hate.

4

(1 mark)

5 Write the **nouns** that can be made from the verbs below.

create _____

intend _____

pursue _____

5

(1 mark)

Top tips

- Look out for adjectives that are similar to abstract nouns (e.g. *angry* and *anger*).
- Check if a word is an abstract noun by putting *the* in front of it (e.g. *the anger, the excitement*).

/ 5

Total for this page

Adjectives

To achieve the higher score, you need to know what adjectives are and how to use them.

1 Circle all the **adjectives** in the sentence below.

The cheering crowds waved and smiled as the victorious team made a special procession through their home town.

1

(1 mark)

2 Tick one box in each row to show whether the underlined words are **adjectives** or **verbs**.

Sentence	Adjective	Verb
The running water overflowed the top of the bath.		
The dog buried a bone beneath the tree.		
You must radio for help as soon as you can.		
Never trust a smiling crocodile.		

2

(1 mark)

3 Underline all the **adjectives** in the passage below.

On our country walk, we spotted an unusually large bird. It sat upon a branch. When the bird stretched its wings, they were wider than my outstretched arms.

3

(1 mark)

4 Tick one box in each row to show whether the underlined words are **adjectives** or **adverbs**.

Sentence	Adjective	Adverb
Once we heard the new baby was born, we went straight to see her.		
This will be a great advertising opportunity for our product.		
In every competition someone has to come first and someone last.		

4

(1 mark)

Top tip
- Decide what a word is doing in a sentence before deciding if it is an adjective.

/ 4

Total for this page

Adverbs

To achieve the higher score, you need to know what adverbs are and how to use them.

1   Underline all the **adverbs** in this passage.

The curtains slowly opened and the stage was completely empty. The audience wondered what would happen next. Then, a small figure walked uncertainly to the centre of the stage.

1

(1 mark)

2   Tick three boxes to show which sentences contain **adverbs**.

Tick **three**.

The artist had carefully crafted a beautiful pot. ☐

We hope that you will have a safe journey. ☐

I hoped the phone would ring soon. ☐

How fast was the car travelling when it hit the tree? ☐

2

(1 mark)

3   Rewrite the sentence below, using a different **adverb**. Remember to punctuate your answer correctly.

You worked hard today.

3

(1 mark)

4   Tick one box in each row to show whether the underlined words are **adjectives** or **adverbs**.

Sentence	Adjective	Adverb
The tourist was <u>completely</u> confused by my directions.		
After a long list, the teacher finally gave the <u>last</u> instruction.		
Because he didn't listen to the directions, Sam took a <u>wrong</u> turn.		
You have done <u>well</u> to pass the test.		

4

(1 mark)

> ★ **Top tip**
> • **Watch out:** Don't miss common adverbs that refer to *when* something happens: *after, before, later, now, soon, yet.*

/ 4

Total for
this page

Modal verbs

To achieve the higher score, you need to know what modal verbs are and how to use them to show possibility.

1 Which of the events in the sentences below is **most likely** to happen?

Tick **one**.

The painter could fall from that ladder if he's not careful. ☐

I think Joe can score a goal in today's match. ☐

I will make you a lovely milkshake when we get home. ☐

We might have to cancel our walk if this rain persists. ☐

2 Rewrite the sentence below, changing the **modal verb**. Remember to punctuate your answer correctly.

They will visit us tomorrow.

_____

3 Rewrite the sentence below, adding a **modal verb**. Remember to punctuate your answer correctly.

The ducks come if you throw them some bread.

_____

_____

4 Underline the **modal verbs** in the sentence below.

We could go across the park to get to the station. It might not seem much of a shortcut, but we can run through the park, which is difficult to do on the pavement.

Adverbials

To achieve the higher score, you need to identify and construct adverbials.

1 Circle the **adverbial phrase** in the sentence below.

If you wait, you'll see the bats that come out after dark.

1
(1 mark)

2 Add a suitable **adverbial** to complete the sentence below.

The museum opens a new exhibition _____ .

2
(1 mark)

3 Reorder the sentence below so that it has a **fronted adverbial**. Remember to use correct capital letters and punctuation.

Alice gritted her teeth and marched off with great determination.

_____

3
(1 mark)

4 Explain the function of the underlined **adverbial** in the sentence below.

The weather had become worse <u>towards the end of the week</u>.

_____

_____

4
(1 mark)

5 Rewrite the sentence below, changing the position of the **adverbial**. Remember to punctuate your answer correctly.

Full of enthusiasm, the team ran out onto the pitch.

_____

5
(1 mark)

6 Insert an appropriate **fronted adverbial** to complete the sentence below. Remember to punctuate your answer correctly.

_____ we went to visit an art exhibition.

6
(1 mark)

Top tip
- To help you find the adverbial, ask questions about the verb. *How? When? Where? Why?*

/ 6

Total for
this page

Pronouns

To achieve the higher score, you need to know what pronouns are and how to use them.

1 Tick one box in each row to show whether each sentence contains a **pronoun** or not.

Sentence	Pronoun	No pronoun
There are various theories about the extinction of dinosaurs.		
Spending too much time on a computer can give you a headache.		
The boat leaves for France in two hours.		
They were able to take pictures of whales on their holiday.		

☐ 1
(1 mark)

2 Circle all the **pronouns** in the passage below.

Edward and Abigail were having a party. They had invited everyone from school. She wanted to play tennis but he would prefer party games.

☐ 2
(1 mark)

3 Tick one box to show the **pronouns** that complete the sentence below.

The musicians were tuning _____ instruments before

_____ performance began so that _____ would

be in tune.

our / a / us ☐   his / my / I ☐   your / their / it ☐   their / the / they ☐

☐ 3
(1 mark)

4 Explain why the underlined **pronoun** is used in the passage below.

Alexandra was ready for the match. <u>She</u> was looking forward to it.

☐ 4
(1 mark)

_____

⭐ **Top tips**

- **Watch out:** *It's* is a subject pronoun and a verb (e.g. *It's* (*It is*) *my birthday.*). *Its* is a possessive pronoun (e.g. *The car has lost its wheel.*).
- You can decide if a word is a pronoun by testing whether you can replace it with a noun.

/ 4

Total for this page

Prepositions

To achieve the higher score, you need to know what prepositions are and be able to use them.

1 Circle all the **prepositions** in the sentence below.

Felix was sitting beside the teacher. He could see the park in the distance through the open window and imagined he was there, playing on the swings.

(1 mark) 1

2 Add a suitable **preposition** to the gaps in the passage below. Use each preposition only once.

The ducks are swimming _____ the pond but the geese are feeding _____ the trees, where people have dropped bread _____ their sandwiches.

(1 mark) 2

3 Rewrite the sentence below, changing the **preposition**.

I put my book beneath my bed.

_____

(1 mark) 3

4 Complete the sentence below, using *after* as a **preposition**.

I will finish my homework after _____.

(1 mark) 4

5 Tick one box in each row to show whether the word <u>until</u> is used as a **preposition** or as a **subordinating conjunction**.

(1 mark) 5

Sentence	Preposition	Subordinating conjunction
We can't leave for the airport <u>until</u> I find the passports.		
You can stay up <u>until</u> midnight on New Year's Eve.		
Sam is visiting his grandma <u>until</u> the weekend.		

Top tip

- **Watch out:** Some words can be used as both prepositions and conjunctions: *before*, *after*, *until*.

/5

Total for this page

Determiners

To achieve the higher score, you need to know what determiners are and how to use them.

1 Add the correct **determiners** from the box to the passage below.

the   some   any

Alex wanted to make _____ cakes but there weren't

_____ eggs in _____ house.

2 Underline all the **determiners** in the passage below.

These computer games are more fun than mine. I haven't bought any new ones lately so mine are old-fashioned.

3 Tick two sentences that use <u>that</u> as a **determiner**.

Tick **two**.

You can't do <u>that</u>. ☐

Sam can carry <u>that</u> bag for you. ☐

<u>That</u> smoothie tastes delicious. ☐

The only bread <u>that</u> is left is mouldy. ☐

4 Rewrite the sentence below, changing the **determiner**. Remember to punctuate your answer correctly.

I really like these shoes.

5 Circle all the **determiners** in the passage below.

The detectives couldn't find any evidence of a burglary so they returned to their police station.

★ **Top tips**

- **Watch out:** Some words can be pronouns and determiners. A determiner is used before a noun phrase; a pronoun is not (e.g. *please pass me that book* (determiner); *you can't do that* (pronoun)).
- Determiners that refer to quantity can be the hardest to spot.
- Always check through the use of all words that could be determiners.

Subordinating and coordinating conjunctions

To achieve the higher score, you need to recognise and use the different conjunctions.

1 Tick one box in each row of the table to show whether the underlined words are **coordinating** or **subordinating conjunctions**.

1

(1 mark)

Sentence	Coordinating conjunction	Subordinating conjunction
The recent storms could have caused a lot of damage <u>but</u> we were very lucky.		
In Australia, visitors can trek up mountains <u>or</u> visit beautiful cities.		
At night, we can see lots of stars <u>if</u> the sky is clear.		
We can eat our sandwiches on the beach <u>unless</u> the tide is in.		

2 Underline all the **conjunctions** in the passage below.

Insects can be fascinating when you study them. Because they are small, their beauty can be best appreciated under a microscope, or you could use a magnifying glass. However, some people are afraid of them.

2

(1 mark)

3 Rewrite the sentence below, changing the **conjunction** for another that makes sense. Remember to punctuate your answer correctly.

We can go swimming when you come to visit me.

3

(1 mark)

4 Tick two boxes to show the sentences that are using the underlined words as **conjunctions**.

Tick **two**.

The rain was heavy <u>but</u> we stayed dry. ☐

Don't open your presents <u>until</u> Christmas day. ☐

The musician left the stage <u>after</u> the applause finished. ☐

You should eat breakfast <u>before</u> school. ☐

4

(1 mark)

/ 4

Total for this page

Main clauses and subordinate clauses

To achieve the higher score, you need to recognise and use main and subordinate clauses.

1 Add the correct words to complete the **subordinate clauses** in the passage below.

| if   although   which |

The museum has a variety of exciting exhibitions _____ the most popular is the Roman village _____ is located on the ground floor. School groups are invited to dress up in Roman clothing _____ the pupils would like to do so.

1

(1 mark)

2 Underline the **subordinate clause** in the sentence below.

I become nervous whenever I have to speak to the whole class.

2

(1 mark)

3 Tick one box in each row to show whether the underlined clause is a **main clause** or a **subordinate clause**.

3

(1 mark)

Sentence	Main clause	Subordinate clause
<u>The summer weather is usually warm</u> although sometimes we get rain.		
<u>If you scatter breadcrumbs on the grass</u>, the ducks will come out of the pond.		
We won't need to bring wellies <u>unless it rains</u>.		
<u>Picking up litter is a school rule.</u>		

4 Rewrite the sentence below to place the **subordinate clause** first. Remember to punctuate your answer correctly.

I will help you if you will let me.

4

(1 mark)

Top tips

- Do the clauses make a complete sentence on their own? If so, they are main clauses. If not, they are subordinate clauses.
- A subordinate clause begins with a subordinating conjunction such as *while, if, when, because.*

/ 4

Total for this page

Relative clauses

To achieve the higher score, you need to recognise and use relative clauses.

1 Which of these sentences contain a **relative clause**?

Tick **two**.

While the class watched, the scientist conducted an experiment. ☐

The telephone rang just as we were about to leave the house. ☐

The acrobat who is wearing the red shirt is the best. ☐

The house in which my grandad lives is over 300 years old. ☐

1

(1 mark)

2 Add the correct **relative pronouns** to the passage below.

| who   that   when |

The photograph _____ is hanging in the school hall

reminds us of the day _____ the Queen came to visit. All

the visitors _____ walk past it comment on it.

2

(1 mark)

3 Tick one box in each row of the table to show whether the word that is used to introduce a **relative clause** or as a **determiner**.

3

(1 mark)

Sentence	Relative clause	Determiner
The judge preferred <u>that</u> picture to this one.		
Games of chess <u>that</u> last for hours are hard work.		
I would like to watch <u>that</u> film at the weekend.		
The door <u>that</u> leads to the fire escape should never be locked.		

Top tip

- *That* is not always a relative pronoun. It can be a determiner (see page 13), (e.g. I like *that* picture). To check whether it begins a relative clause, check if it is followed by a verb (e.g. I like the picture *that is hanging in the hall*).

/ 3

Total for this page

Noun phrases

To achieve the higher score, you need to recognise and use noun phrases.

1 Underline all the words that make the **noun phrase** in the sentence below.

The sprinting cheetah was travelling incredibly fast.

2 Circle all the **noun phrases** in the sentence below.

While a crescent moon hung in the sky, wolves' cries echoed through the forest.

3 Expand the underlined **noun phrase** in the sentence below. Write the new phrase on the line below.

The waves crashed onto the beach during the storm.

4 Rewrite the sentence below, adding to the **noun phrase**. Remember to punctuate your answer correctly.

I saw some butterflies yesterday.

5 Which of the sentences below contain **noun phrases**?

Tick **two**.

Large dogs are not allowed in the playground. ☐

Please give it to me. ☐

Finlay took his brother's new computer game. ☐

You are taller and stronger than me. ☐

6 Write a **noun phrase** containing at least three words to complete the sentence below. Remember to punctuate your answer correctly.

We saw _____ at the zoo last week.

Subject and object

To achieve the higher score, you need to identify the subject and object of sentences.

1 Write **S** (**subject**) or **O** (**object**) in the boxes below the sentence.

Josh was making faces at the monkeys in the zoo, but they did not

☐   ☐   ☐

copy him.

☐

☐ 1

(1 mark)

2 Rewrite the sentence below, changing the **object**. Remember to punctuate your answer correctly.

The rabbits escaped from the hutch.

☐ 2

(1 mark)

3 Circle all the **subjects** in the passage below.

While he was waiting for his mum, Oscar listened to the radio in the car. Alysha, his favourite singer, was talking to the presenter about her music.

☐ 3

(1 mark)

4 Underline the **object** in the sentence below.

Sheena had been hit by a stray football in the playground.

☐ 4

(1 mark)

5 Tick one box in each row to show whether Kazim is a **subject** or an **object** in the sentences below.

☐ 5

(1 mark)

Sentence	Subject	Object
I can't see Kazim anywhere.		
If Kazim studies hard, he'll pass the test.		
We'll collect Kazim on our way to school.		
Kazim was being pushed along by the crowd.		

☐ / 5

Total for this page

Subject and verb agreement

To achieve the higher score, you need to make the subject and verb of a sentence agree.

1   Tick the sentences that are correct.

Spring flowers are beginning to bloom in the garden. ☐

At the opening ceremony, each team of competitors marches past the judges. ☐

Members of the local council is coming to visit our school next week. ☐

Children should enter through the doors near the playground. ☐

☐ 1
(1 mark)

2   Circle the correct words to complete the sentences below.

Although a bunch of flowers **make / makes** a lovely 'thank you' gift for a teacher, some people **prefer / prefers** a box of chocolates. However, my teacher **like / likes** a drawing or a poem to remind her of us.

☐ 2
(1 mark)

3   Write <u>is</u> or <u>are</u> in the gaps in the sentences below to make the **subject** and **verb** agree.

A swarm of wasps _____ gathering in the roof of our house.

The government _____ led by the Prime Minister.

A school of dolphins _____ swimming near our boat.

Police officers _____ trained to deal with difficult situations.

☐ 3
(1 mark)

Top tip
- Focus on the first part of the noun phrase, e.g. *herd* of goats, *collections* of pictures, to know whether to use a plural or singular verb form.

/3

Total for this page

Verbs in the progressive and perfect tenses

To achieve the higher score, you need to recognise the present and past progressive tenses and the present and past perfect tenses and be able to construct these verb forms.

1 Fill in the gaps in the sentence below, using the **past progressive** form of the verbs in the boxes.

> **to work**
> ↓

While I _____ hard on my homework, my sister

> **to relax**
> ↓

_____ on the sofa watching television.

2 Fill in the gaps in the sentence below, using the **present perfect** form of the verbs in the boxes.

> **to learn**
> ↓

Leo _____ his lines for the school play and his dad

> **to help**
> ↓

_____ him to make his costume.

3 In the sentence below, Ella laid the table before she changed for her party. Complete the sentence with the correct **verb form**.

> **to lay**
> ↓

After Ella _____ the table, she changed for her party.

4 Tick the boxes that show the sentences that contain verbs in the **progressive forms**.

My headache is hurting a lot this afternoon. ☐

I always have a shower before I go to bed. ☐

The seals were waiting for the keepers to feed them. ☐

All of the children ran out to play in the snow. ☐

Passive and active voices

To achieve the higher score, you need to recognise the active and passive voice.

1   Tick one box in each row of the table to show whether each sentence is in the **active** or the **passive** voice.

Sentence	Active	Passive
The police were quickly called to the accident on the motorway.		
Planes were flying low and doing stunts at the air show.		
A new treatment for flu has been discovered by international scientists.		
The vets at the surgery are busy helping to deliver a litter of kittens.		

1
(1 mark)

2   Which option completes the sentence below in the **passive** voice?

Despite his best efforts, Tristan

                                    Tick **one**.

lost the match. ☐

was beaten. ☐

could not win the match. ☐

would have to play another match. ☐

2
(1 mark)

3   Rewrite the sentence below in the **passive** voice. Remember to punctuate your answer correctly.

A gust of wind blew shut the window.

3
(1 mark)

4   Rewrite the sentence below in the **active** voice. Remember to punctuate your answer correctly.

The remains of the cake were eaten by the dog.

4
(1 mark)

/ 4

Total for
this page

Subjunctive verb forms

To achieve the higher score, you need to recognise verbs in the subjunctive form.

1 Which option completes the sentence below so that it uses the **subjunctive** form?

Billy wished he _____ able to run as fast as his sister.

were ☐   was ☐   could be ☐   may be ☐

1 (1 mark)

2 Write the correct form of the verb in the gap below so that it uses the **subjunctive** mood.

to clean

The dentist recommended that Elisha _____ her teeth more thoroughly to avoid a filling.

2 (1 mark)

3 Which of the sentences below is written in the **subjunctive** mood?

The astronomer had been able to see a shooting star as the night was so clear. ☐

If you are here on time, you will be able to watch the start of the film. ☐

Jessica's grandad suggested that she save a little money each week for her holiday. ☐

While Joe was clearing up, his brother just played on the computer. ☐

3 (1 mark)

4 Rewrite the verb underlined in the sentence below so that it uses the **subjunctive** mood.

Eddie's teacher insisted that he <u>wears</u> school uniform the same as anyone else. _____

4 (1 mark)

5 Rewrite the sentence below so that it uses the **subjunctive** mood. Remember to punctuate your answer correctly.

I would get that cut looked at by a doctor if I was you.

5 (1 mark)

/ 5

Total for this page

Standard English and formality

To achieve the higher score, you need to know how to identify and use Standard English, and to identify differences between informal and formal language.

1 Circle one word in each underlined pair to complete the sentences using **Standard English**.

I would like the cake **that / what** is in the window.

We all **did / done** our work in extra quick time.

2 Rewrite the sentence below using **Standard English**. Remember to punctuate your answer correctly.

I have less sweets than you.

3 Circle the word to complete the sentence using the most **formal** language.

The office will telephone you to **give / confirm** the time of your appointment.

4 Explain the effect of changing the words underlined in the sentences below.

Archie gave a speech to express his <u>thanks</u> for the prize.

Archie gave a speech to express his <u>gratitude</u> for the prize.

5 Rewrite the sentence below using **Standard English**. Remember to punctuate your answer correctly.

I ain't got nothing for you.

Capital letters, full stops, exclamation marks and question marks

To achieve the higher score, you need to use capital letters, full stops, exclamation marks and question marks in the right places in sentences.

1 Which sentence uses **capital letters** correctly?

Tick **one**.

In the Autumn, Heath School will teach Chinese and art. ☐

In the Autumn, Heath school will teach Chinese and art. ☐

In the Autumn, Heath School will teach Chinese and Art. ☐

In the autumn, Heath School will teach Chinese and art. ☐

1 (1 mark)

2 Circle the words that should have **capital letters** in the passage below.

Our cousin, kim, is opening a new business called precious pets. It will open at the end of spring, in april, in a shop on norris street.

2 (1 mark)

3 Explain why the words underlined should have a **capital letter**.

At <u>Christmas</u> we will be going to visit our cousins in <u>Scotland</u>.

Christmas _____

Scotland _____

3 (1 mark)

4 Tick the sentence that must end with an **exclamation mark**.

Tick **one**.

Nice to meet you ☐

Can you believe it ☐

What an amazing book this is ☐

I thought we had won ☐

4 (1 mark)

> ★ **Top tip**
> - Remember that all parts of proper nouns need capital letters (e.g. *Sally Smith, United Kingdom, Rising Stars Publications*).

/4

Total for this page

Commas

To achieve the higher score, you need to use commas to mark clauses or phrases, to separate items in a list and to clarify meanings.

1   Tick one box to show why **commas** have been used in the sentence below.

    Unless the fire engine arrives soon, the flames will destroy the shed.

    Tick **one**.

    to introduce a piece of speech   ☐

    to mark a clause   ☐

    to separate items in a list   ☐

    to separate two sentences   ☐

    ☐ 1
    (1 mark)

2   Add **commas** to the passage below.

    Alfie uses a telescope to see the night sky the moon and the stars. Whenever the night is clear he looks at the stars.

    ☐ 2
    (1 mark)

3   Insert a **comma** to demonstrate that the speaker is talking directly to Lucy.

    Now that I've heard the explanation I understand Lucy.

    ☐ 3
    (1 mark)

4   Insert **commas** in the sentence below.

    Packing the shopping carefully placing items such as the eggs on the top the twins were showing how sensible they could be.

    ☐ 4
    (1 mark)

5   Explain how a **comma** changes the meaning of the sentence below.

    Will you help, Mark?
    Will you help Mark?

    ☐ 5
    (1 mark)

⬥ **Top tips**

• Remember to use two commas to mark an embedded clause or phrase (e.g. *Oscar, my favourite cat, often sits on my shoulder.*).
• Look out for adverbial phrases and clauses that require a comma (e.g. *Suddenly, I saw it. Next, it saw me.*).

/ 5

Total for this page

25

Inverted commas

To achieve the higher score, you need to use inverted commas to show direct speech.

1 Which of the sentences below are correctly punctuated? Tick **two**.

"Could dragons once have walked the earth, like dinosaurs?" wondered Angel. ☐

Angel wondered, "Could dragons once have walked the earth, like dinosaurs"? ☐

"Could dragons once have walked the earth, like dinosaurs," wondered Angel? ☐

Angel wondered, "Could dragons once have walked the earth, like dinosaurs?" ☐

☐ 1

(1 mark)

2 Rewrite the sentence below, using correct punctuation for **direct speech**.

Don't forget to fill up with fuel before your journey reminded Mum

☐ 2

(1 mark)

3 Which of the sentences below are correctly punctuated?

"Hurry up," called Elizabeth, "or we will be late." ☐

Zach wanted to know "when he was supposed to begin the game?" ☐

Peter asked if the game had already started. ☐

"If you continue to blow up that balloon" warned Ali, "it will burst." ☐

☐ 3

(1 mark)

4 Rewrite the sentence below, putting the police officer's words into **direct speech**. Remember to punctuate your answer correctly.

The police officer said that the burglar had not managed to steal anything despite the broken window.

☐ 4

(1 mark)

⭐ **Top tip**

- If you place the commas first, it is easier to make sure they are correctly inside or outside the speech marks.

/ 4

Total for this page

Apostrophes

To achieve the higher score, you need to use apostrophes correctly.

1 Tick one box in each row to show how the **apostrophe** has been used in the sentence.

Sentence	To show omission	To show possession
He couldn't climb the wall.		
That is the dog's bowl.		
Let's go to your house.		
It's my turn.		

1 (1 mark)

2 Circle the words in the sentence below that should be written with **apostrophes**.

Ive left the childrens coats behind so they wont be able to go outside.

2 (1 mark)

3 Rewrite the sentence below, correctly using **apostrophes**.

Todays sunshine isnt expected at this time of year but its very welcome.

3 (1 mark)

_____

_____

4 Explain why **apostrophes** are used in the sentence below.

I wouldn't believe everything that John's brother says.

wouldn't _____

John's _____

4 (1 mark)

> **Top tips**
> - Beware of words that join together or change when the apostrophe is added (e.g. *could not = couldn't*; *will not = won't*).
> - **Watch out:** *Its* and *it's* are often confused. *It's* is *it is* shortened. *Its* is used for possession. There is no apostrophe in *its*, for possession.
> - **Watch out:** Apostrophes of possession can be tricky with plurals (e.g. *Foxes' tails are bushy* but *The fox's tail was injured.*).

/4

Total for this page

Parenthesis

To achieve the higher score, you need to recognise the correct use of a parenthesis.

1 Which of these sentences uses **commas** correctly? Tick **one**.

James despite being the chattiest boy, in the class, ☐
still managed to complete his work on time.

James despite being the chattiest boy in the class, ☐
still managed to complete his work, on time.

James, despite being the chattiest boy in the class, ☐
still managed to complete his work on time.

James, despite being the chattiest boy in the class ☐
still managed to complete his work, on time.

☐ 1

(1 mark)

2 Rewrite the sentence below, correctly adding two **dashes**.

When we go on safari, I hope to see some big animals maybe an
elephant, rhino or hippo and take photos.

☐ 2

(1 mark)

3 Add **brackets** to the sentence below.

Before we leave on holiday, my dad goes through his checklist
passport, tickets, toothbrush as he starts the car.

☐ 3

(1 mark)

4 Which sentences are correctly punctuated?   Tick **two**.

The tight-rope walker, wobbled wildly, on the wire. ☐

Clowns are popular with some people, but – perhaps ☐
surprisingly – others find them rather scary.

Please buy your tickets (available from May 20th) ☐
from the booking office or online.

The gymnasts tumbled around the circus ring ☐
(to the delight) of the audience.

☐ 4

(1 mark)

5 Explain why **parenthesis** has been used in the sentence below.

Many members of the family (grandparents, cousins, aunts and uncles)
are coming to the party.

☐ 5

(1 mark)

☐ / 5

*Total for
this page*

Colons, semi-colons, single dashes, hyphens and bullet points

To achieve the higher score, you need to recognise and use these punctuation marks correctly.

1   Tick one box to show the sentence that is correctly punctuated.

Tick **one**.

Daniel went to the doctor's; with a dreadful cough. He was given medicine to take daily. ☐

Daniel went to the doctor's with a dreadful cough; he was given medicine to take daily. ☐

Daniel; went to the doctor's with a dreadful cough. He was given medicine to take daily. ☐

Daniel went to the doctor's with a dreadful cough, He was given medicine to take; daily. ☐

1

(1 mark)

2   Add a **single dash** to the sentence below.

At the weekend, we went to the beach and looked for interesting stones beneath the cliffs it was a lovely day.

2

(1 mark)

3   To make a cake, Benny needs four ingredients: eggs, sugar, butter and flour.

Finish the recipe below, writing the ingredients as a list with **bullet points**.

To make your cake, you will need these ingredients:

- _____
- _____
- _____
- _____

3

(1 mark)

4   Rewrite the information below, correctly using a **colon**.

For her birthday, we bought my grandma her favourite flowers (daffodils, tulips and roses).

_____

_____

4

(1 mark)

/ 4

Total for this page

29

Prefixes and suffixes

To achieve the higher score, you need to add prefixes and suffixes to words.

1 Which **prefix** can be added to both of the words below?

_____septic

_____social

Prefix: _____

2 Add **suffixes** to make these words into nouns.

joyful_____

direct_____

build_____

3 Which **prefix** can be added to both of the words below?

_____charge

_____qualify

Prefix: _____

4 Add a **prefix** from the box to each of the words below to make a new word.

Use each prefix only once.

| aqua   sub   auto |

_____graph

_____aqua

_____marine

5 Write a word that has the same **suffix** as the word below.

forgiveness

_____

Prefixes

To achieve the higher score, you need to correctly spell words with prefixes.

1 Add the <u>dis</u> **prefix** to these words to make new words. Write a sentence for each one. Remember to punctuate your answers correctly.

appointment _____

arm _____

connect _____

courage _____

honourable _____

1

(1 mark)

2 Circle the correct spelling in each sentence.

a) You must **disclose/desclose** any information you have about the crime.

b) Alfie has always been a **discontented/descontented** child.

c) The robber has been **ditained/detained** by the police.

d) The earthquake caused much **destruction/distruction**.

e) After the fire, the landscape lay **desolate/disolate** and bare.

2

(1 mark)

3 Write the words below adding the correct **prefix** from the box.

| in   im   il   ir |

a) excusable _____

b) pertinent _____

c) reverent _____

d) perfect _____

e) legal _____

f) logical _____

g) possible _____

h) direct _____

3

(1 mark)

Top tips

- When a word begins with *dis*, you can usually remove the *dis* and a root word will still exist. When a word begins with *des*, it doesn't usually make sense if you remove *des*.
- Remember to keep the double letter if the prefix ends and the word begins with the same letter.
- Prefixes have different meanings: *re* = again or back   *sub* = under   *inter* = between   *super* = above   *anti* = against   *auto* = self

/3

Total for this page

31

Suffixes: *-tion, -ssion, -cian*

To achieve the higher score, you need to correctly spell words containing these suffixes.

1   Sort the words below into four groups and then add them to the table, including the correct **suffix**.

1

(2 marks)

apprehend   permit   express   persuade   politic   divert

exhibit   possess   electric   ascend   decide   extend

inject   confuse

Ends in <u>d</u>, <u>de</u> or <u>se</u>	Ends in <u>c</u> or <u>cs</u>	Ends in <u>ss</u> or <u>mit</u>	Ends in another way

2   Select the correct spellings in the sentences below. Write the correct word on the line.

2

(1 mark)

a)   This story contains too much **repetition / repeatition**.

_____

b)   There will need to be considerable **adaption / adaptation** to make this building suitable for a wheelchair.

_____

c)   There was a huge **expulsion / expelsion** of gases from the volcano.

_____

d)   The scientist, Charles Darwin, developed a theory about **evolution / evolvution**.

_____

> ## Top tips
> - *-tion* is the most common ending to make the sound 'shun'.
> - *-sion* is used if the word ends in *d*, *de* or *se*. Remove the final *d*, *de* or *se* and add *-sion*.
> - *-cian* is used if the word ends in *c* or *cs*.
> - *-ssion* is used if the root word ends in *ss* or *mit*.
> - Remember to remove the final letter before the suffix, if necessary.

/ 3

Total for this page

Suffixes: *-ous, -tious, -cious*

To achieve the higher score, you need to correctly spell words containing these suffixes.

1 Draw lines to link the words with similar meanings.

boisterous	well-mannered
callous	hard-hearted
carnivorous	lively
conscious	awake
cautious	meat-eating
momentous	important
courteous	careful

(1 mark) 1

2 Write a sentence using each of the words below. Remember to punctuate your answers correctly.

infectious _____

religious _____

notorious _____

outrageous _____

(4 marks) 2

3 Remind yourself of the rule for words ending in y.

Add the **suffix** -<u>ous</u> to the words below, making any necessary changes.

fury _____

vary _____

glory _____

study _____

injury _____

(1 mark) 3

/ 6

Total for this page

Suffixes: -able, -ably, -ible, -ibly

To achieve the higher score, you need to correctly spell words containing these suffixes.

1 Add the words from the box to the sentences below.

| unreachable   unintelligible   plausible   edible   irreversible |

a) That's a _____ suggestion and it may work.

b) The island was _____ by boat because of the storm.

c) The radio signal was so poor that the voice was _____.

d) Some fungi are _____ but some are poisonous.

e) Once you have accepted the decision, it will be _____.

1

(1 mark)

2 Spot the spelling mistakes in the passage below. Underline them and write the correct spellings on the lines below.

The small child was almost unnoticable until she stepped into the spotlight and began to climb the pole to the trapeze swing. The crowd were understandably hushed, probibly through anxiety that she may fall. It was unbelieveble to see how flexable she was, curling around the swing like a cat.

_____   _____

_____   _____

2

(2 marks)

3 The words below have to be changed before the **suffix** -<u>able</u> is added. Make the change and add the **suffix**.

classify _____   envy _____

identify _____   pity _____

rely _____

Write each word in a sentence.

_____

_____

_____

_____

3

(6 marks)

/9

Total for this page

Suffixes: *-ant, -ance, -ancy, -ent, -ence, -ency*

To achieve the higher score, you need to correctly spell words containing these suffixes.

1 Match these words with the one most **similar** in meaning.

preference	life
advance	choice
magnificent	go forwards
conference	wonderful
existence	meeting
incompetence	failure

2 Select the words from the box to complete the sentences.

absent   audience   diligently   performance   interference persistently

Although Nisha had been _____ from the rehearsals, she had _____ learned her lines ready for the _____. However, one member of the _____ was causing great _____ in the show as he was _____ calling out the endings to Nisha's jokes.

3 Circle the correct spelling.

transparant	transparent
acquaintance	acquantence
resistence	resistance
perseverence	perseverance
vigilent	vigilant
insignificant	insignificent

Words with *ie, ei, eigh, ey, ay*

To achieve the higher score, you need to correctly spell words containing these combinations of letters.

1 Add <u>ie</u> or <u>ei</u> to the words below.

a) What a super ach_____vement.

b) It is not conven_____nt to see you now.

c) We can get a cour_____r to deliver the urgent parcel.

d) My n_____ce is two tomorrow.

e) The fire is burning f_____rcely.

2 Organise these words into two groups within the table.

ceiling   alien   protein   counterfeit   hygienic   deceitful

relieve   Einstein   foreigner   height   field   heiress

<u>ei</u> words	<u>ie</u> words

3 Complete the sentences below using words from the table.

a) A female who inherits is an _____.

b) Fake money is _____.

c) A famous scientist: Albert _____.

d) Keeping things clean is _____.

e) If you visit another country, you will be a _____.

1 ☐ 1 *(1 mark)*

2 ☐ 2 *(2 marks)*

3 ☐ 3 *(1 mark)*

/ 4

Total for this page

Words with *ough*

To achieve the higher score, you need to correctly spell words containing this combination of letters.

1 Complete the sentences using the <u>ough</u> words in the box.

drought boughs afterthought enough hiccoughs wrought

a) I have _____ sweets for everyone.

b) Some _____ were damaged in last night's storm.

c) I have a terrible case of the _____ .

d) The gate to the castle was made of _____ iron.

e) "Thank you," said Tom as an _____ .

f) The lack of rain is causing a dreadful _____ .

(1 mark)

2 Match each <u>ough</u> word with a suffix from the box and write the new word on the line.

en ful ness est

rough _____   thorough _____

tough _____   thoughtful _____

2
(1 mark)

3 Use the dictionary to help you match these unusual <u>ough</u> words with their meanings.

brougham		a period of leave for a soldier
thoroughfare		a roadway
doughty		hardy, brave
furlough		a type of horse-drawn carriage
slough off		a type of racehorse
thoroughbred		get rid of

3
(1 mark)

/3

Word endings: *al, el, il, le*

To achieve the higher score, you need to correctly spell words that end with these letters.

1 Match the words with their meanings.

anvil	a type of bag
uncivil	impolite
abnormal	a blacksmith's tool
cardinal	a high-status job in the church
admiral	an officer in the navy
satchel	unusual

1

(1 mark)

2 Complete the words by adding the correct two letters.

foss_ _   carous_ _

aeri_ _   mythic_ _

applicab_ _   barr_ _

coast_ _   terrib_ _

presidenti_ _   parall_ _

profession_ _   archaeologic_ _

icic_ _   squirr_ _

sentiment_ _

2

(1 mark)

3 Complete the sentences below with the correct word from the box.

criminal   audible   carousel   peril

Please speak up as you are barely _____.

A _____ is someone who has broken the law.

Be careful. You are in _____ of falling off the cliff.

We will have a _____ of activities that change each hour.

3

(1 mark)

/3

Total for this page

Silent letters

To achieve the higher score, you need to correctly spell words containing silent letters.

1 Circle the **silent letter** in each word.

a) handkerchief

b) scene

c) scissors

d) hymn

e) crumb

f) fascinate

g) campaign

h) solemn

i) guilt

1
(1 mark)

2 Add the missing **silent letter** to the words below.

a) w_istle

b) g_ess

c) _nome

d) tom_

e) cres_ent

f) desi_n

g) san_wich

h) lis_en

i) _nowledge

j) rog_e

2
(1 mark)

3 Write sentences that include the pairs of words below. Remember to punctuate your answers correctly.

a) anchor   glistening

_____

b) rustle   doubt

_____

c) stomach   aches

_____

d) sword   knight

_____

e) wretched   solemn

_____

3
(5 marks)

/ 7

Total for
this page

Homophones

To achieve the higher score, you need to correctly spell a variety of homophones.

1 Write the correct spelling of the word that is used incorrectly.

  a) What have you written on the bored?

    _____

  b) A dessert can get very cold at night.

    _____

  c) We except all clothing donations as long as they are in bags.

    _____

  d) The cue for the favourite ride at the fair was very long.

    _____

  e) The traffic was stationery for an hour.

    _____

2 Write the **homophone** for the words given below.

loan	_____	alter	_____
maid	_____	seam	_____
bawled	_____	sighed	_____
bear	_____	sole	_____

3 Select a word from the box to complete the sentences.

> maize maze missed mist seize sees sort sought sheikh shake

  a) The _____ is ripening in the sun and will soon be ready to pick.

  b) A _____ was falling across the valleys.

  c) Joe took the opportunity to _____ the rugby ball and run with it.

  d) What _____ of car is your favourite?

  e) Give the rug a good _____ to remove the dust.

Synonyms and antonyms

To achieve the higher score, you need to know the terms synonym and antonym, and identify examples.

1 Tick the word closest in meaning to <u>concur</u>.

agree ☐   conquer ☐

argue ☐   cure ☐

2 Draw a line to match each word to its opposite meaning.

wandering	abandon
aggressive	direct
achieve	pacifying
durable	weak

3 Which word is the **antonym** of <u>deny</u>?

attempt ☐   invite ☐

confirm ☐   recognise ☐

4 Which word is a **synonym** of <u>antiquated</u>?

old-fashioned ☐

half-hearted ☐

open-minded ☐

sharply dressed ☐

5 Match the words below with their **synonyms**.

comply	persuade
coerce	agree
corrupt	organise
collate	destroy

Top tip

- Remember: *S* for synonym, *S* for same. *A* for antonym, *A* for against.

Word families

To achieve the higher score, you need to know words which share the same root word or prefix.

1   Tick the words that belong to the same **word family**.

correction ☐

correspondent ☐

correspondence ☐

core ☐

2   Write the **root word** for this word family.

delivery   deliverable

_____

3   Add another word to this **word family**.

improve   improving

_____

4   What does the root <u>cover</u> mean in the **word family** below?

discovery   covering   uncover

Tick **one**.

clothe ☐

hide ☐

make ☐

reveal ☐

5   Write a sentence using the word <u>curve</u> as a **noun**. Remember to punctuate your answer correctly.

_____

6   Write a sentence using the word <u>curve</u> as a **verb**. Remember to punctuate your answer correctly.

_____

Answers

All answers are worth 1 mark, unless otherwise indicated.

Nouns (page 6)
1 Accept a sentence that makes sense, using 'rush' as a noun, e.g. I was in a great rush. The sentence must be correctly punctuated.
2 tick: We have a strict bedtime routine.
   Your rudeness is becoming a problem.
3 Accept answers that change the noun 'confusion' for another that makes sense, e.g. problem; idea; question. The sentence must be correctly punctuated.
4 underline: poem; range; feelings; love; hate
5 creation; intention; pursuit

Adjectives (page 7)
1 circle: cheering; victorious; special; home
2 The running water overflowed the top of the bath. adjective
   The dog buried a bone beneath the tree. verb
   You must radio for help as soon as you can. verb
   Never trust a smiling crocodile. adjective
3 underline: country; large; wider; outstretched
4 Once we heard the new baby was born, we went straight to see her. adverb
   This will be a great advertising opportunity for our product. adjective
   In every competition someone has to come first and someone last. adverb

Adverbs (page 8)
1 underline: slowly; completely; next; Then; uncertainly
2 tick: The artist had carefully crafted a beautiful pot.
   I hoped the phone would ring soon.
   How fast was the car travelling when it hit the tree?
3 Accept answers that change 'hard' for another adverb, e.g. well; quickly; poorly. The sentence must be correctly spelt and punctuated.

4 The tourist was completely confused by my directions. adverb
   After a long list, the teacher finally gave the last instruction. adjective
   Because he didn't listen to the directions, Sam took a wrong turn. adjective
   You have done well to pass the test. adverb

Modal verbs (page 9)
1 tick: I will make you a lovely milkshake when we get home.
2 Accept answers that change the verb 'will' for another modal, e.g. must; should; could; may; might. The sentence must be correctly spelt and punctuated.
3 Accept answers that add a modal verb before 'come', e.g. may; could; might; will. The sentence must be correctly spelt and punctuated.
4 underline: could; might; can

Adverbials (page 10)
1 circle: after dark
2 Accept answers that give an adverbial and make sense, e.g. at the end of the month; in the top gallery.
3 With great determination, Alice gritted her teeth and marched off. The sentence must be correctly punctuated.
4 Accept answers that refer to the adverbial giving information about time, e.g. it tells you when the action happens.
5 The team ran out onto the pitch, full of enthusiasm. / The team, full of enthusiasm, ran out onto the pitch. The sentence must be correctly punctuated.
6 Accept answers that give an appropriate and plausible fronted adverbial demarcated with a comma, e.g.
   • Last week,
   • In November,
   • On Tuesday.
   • After assembly,
   • Curiously,

Pronouns (page 11)
1 There are various theories about the extinction of dinosaurs. no pronoun

Spending too much time on a computer can give you a headache. pronoun
   Our boat leaves for France in two hours. no pronoun
   They were able to take pictures of whales on their holiday. pronoun
2 circle: They; She; he
3 tick: their / the / they
4 Accept answers that explain that the pronoun avoids repetition of the name.

Prepositions (page 12)
1 circle: beside; in; through; on
2 Accept suitable answers, e.g. in the pond / beside; beneath; between the trees / from their sandwiches.
3 Accept suitable answers that make sense, e.g. on; below; beside.
4 Accept answers that follow 'after' with a noun or noun phrase, e.g. lunch; the programme. Do not accept answers that contain a verb, e.g. after I eat my supper.
5 We can't leave for the airport until I find the passports. subordinating conjunction
   You can stay up until midnight on New Year's Eve. preposition
   Sam is visiting his grandma until the weekend. preposition

Determiners (page 13)
1 some; any; the
2 underline: These; any
3 tick: Sam can carry that bag for you. That smoothie tastes delicious.
4 I really like those; the; any shoes. The sentence must be correctly punctuated.
5 circle: The; any; a; their

Subordinating and coordinating conjunctions (page 14)
1 The recent storms could have caused a lot of damage but we were very lucky. coordinating conjunction
   In Australia, visitors can trek up mountains or visit beautiful cities. coordinating conjunction
   At night, we can see lots of stars if the sky is clear. subordinating conjunction

We can eat our sandwiches on the beach <u>unless</u> the tide is in. subordinating conjunction

2 underline: when; Because; or

3 Accept answers that change the conjunction and make sense, e.g. if; as soon as; whenever. The sentence must be correctly punctuated.

4 tick: The rain was heavy <u>but</u> we stayed dry.
The musician left the stage <u>after</u> the applause finished.

Main clauses and subordinate clauses (page 15)

1 although; which; if

2 underline: whenever I have to speak to the whole class

3 <u>The summer weather is usually warm</u> although sometimes we get rain. main clause
<u>If you scatter breadcrumbs on the grass</u>, the ducks will come out of the pond. subordinate clause
We won't need to bring wellies <u>unless it rains</u>. subordinate clause
<u>Picking up litter is a school rule</u>. main clause

4 If you will let me, I will help you. The sentence must be correctly punctuated.

Relative clauses (page 16)

1 tick: The acrobat who is wearing the red shirt is the best.
The house in which my grandad lives is over 300 years old.

2 that; when; who

3 The judge preferred <u>that</u> picture to this one. determiner
Games of chess <u>that</u> last for hours are hard work. relative clause
I would like to watch <u>that</u> film at the weekend. determiner
The door <u>that</u> leads to the fire escape should never be locked. relative clause

Noun phrases (page 17)

1 underline: The sprinting cheetah

2 circle: a crescent moon; in the sky; wolves' cries; through the forest

3 Accept answers that expand 'the waves', e.g. The violent; enormous waves…

4 Accept answers that expand 'butterflies' and make sense, e.g. I saw some beautiful; large; unusual butterflies yesterday. The sentence must be correctly punctuated.

5 tick: Large dogs are not allowed in the playground.
Finlay took his brother's new computer game.

6 Accept answers that give an appropriate and plausible noun phrase containing three words, e.g. some African elephants; three tall giraffes; a cute penguin. The answer must be correctly punctuated and grammatically accurate.

Subject and object (page 18)

1 Josh: subject; monkeys: object; they: subject; him: object

2 Accept suitable answers that change 'hutch' for another object, e.g. The rabbits escaped from the fox; cage; terrible storm. The sentence must be correctly punctuated.

3 circle: he; Oscar; Alysha

4 underline: a stray football

5 I can't see Kazim anywhere. object
If Kazim studies hard, he'll pass the test. subject
We'll collect Kazim on our way to school. object
Kazim was being pushed along by the crowd. subject.

Subject and verb agreement (page 19)

1 tick: Spring flowers are beginning to bloom in the garden.
At the opening ceremony, each team of competitors marches past the judges.
Children should enter through the doors near the playground.

2 circle: makes; prefer; likes

3 is; is; is; are

Verbs in the progressive and perfect tenses (page 20)

1 was working; was relaxing

2 has learned; has helped

3 had laid / had lain

4 tick: My headache is hurting a lot this afternoon.
The seals were waiting for the keepers to feed them.

Passive and active voices (page 21)

1 The police were quickly called to the accident on the motorway. passive
Planes were flying low and doing stunts at the air show. active
A new treatment for flu has been discovered by international scientists. passive
The vets at the surgery are busy helping to deliver a litter of kittens. active

2 tick: was beaten.

3 The window was; has been blown shut by a gust of wind.
The sentence must be correctly punctuated.

4 The dog ate; has eaten the remains of the cake.
The sentence must be correctly punctuated.

Subjunctive verb forms (page 22)

1 tick: were

2 clean

3 tick: Jessica's grandad suggested that she save a little money each week for her holiday.

4 wear

5 I would get that cut looked at by a doctor if I were you.
The sentence must be correctly punctuated.

Standard English and formality (page 23)

1 circle: that; did

2 I have fewer sweets than you. The sentence must be correctly punctuated.

3 circle: confirm

4 Accept an answer that recognises an increase in formality, e.g. The second one is more formal. / The first one is informal and the second is formal.

5 I haven't; have not got anything for you. / I have nothing for you. The sentence must be correctly punctuated.

Capital letters, full stops, exclamation marks and question marks (page 24)

1 tick: In the autumn, Heath School will teach Chinese and art.

2 circle: kim; precious pets; april; norris street

3 Christmas: because it is the name of a festival. Scotland: because it is the name of a country.

4 tick: What an amazing book this is

Commas (page 25)

1 tick: to mark a clause

2 Alfie uses a powerful telescope to see the night sky, the moon and the

stars. Whenever the night is clear, he looks at the stars.

3 Now that I've heard the explanation I understand, Lucy.

4 Packing the shopping carefully, placing items, such as the eggs, on the top, the twins were showing how sensible they could be.

5 Accept answers that show understanding that the comma affects whether Mark is being spoken about, or spoken to directly.

Inverted commas (page 26)

1 tick: "Could dragons once have walked the earth, like dinosaurs?" wondered Angel.
Angel wondered, "Could dragons once have walked the earth, like dinosaurs?"

2 "Don't forget to fill up with fuel before your journey," reminded Mum.
The sentence must be correctly punctuated.

3 tick: "Hurry up," called Elizabeth, "or we will be late."
Peter asked if the game had already started.

4 "The burglar has not managed to steal anything, despite the broken window," said the police officer. / The police officer said, "The burglar has not managed to steal anything, despite the broken window."
The sentence must be correctly punctuated.

Apostrophes (page 27)

1 He couldn't climb the wall. omission
That is the dog's bowl. possession
Let's go to your house. omission
It's my turn. omission

2 circle: Ive; childrens; wont

3 Today's sunshine isn't expected at this time of year but it's very welcome.
The sentence must be correctly spelt and punctuated.

4 wouldn't: apostrophe used for contraction; to replace a missing letter.
John's: apostrophe used to show possession; belonging to someone.

Parenthesis (page 28)

1 tick: James, despite being the chattiest boy in the class, still

managed to complete his work on time.

2 When we go on safari, I hope to see some big animals – maybe an elephant, rhino or hippo – and take photos.

3 Before we leave on holiday, my dad goes through his checklist (passport, tickets, toothbrush) as he starts the car.

4 tick: Clowns are popular with some people, but – perhaps surprisingly – others find them rather scary. Please buy your tickets (available from May 20th) from the booking office or online.

5 Accept answers that show that parenthesis is used to add extra information about 'the family', e.g. it tells who is in the family.

Colons, semi-colons, single dashes, hyphens and bullet points (page 29)

1 tick: Daniel went to the doctor's with a dreadful cough; he was given medicine to take daily.

2 At the weekend, we went to the beach and looked for interesting stones beneath the cliffs – it was a lovely day.

3 Accept answers that use bullet points with consistent punctuation, e.g. with no punctuation on each line, or with commas / semi-colons on each and a full stop on the last.
To make your cake, you will need these ingredients:
  • eggs
  • sugar
  • butter
  • flour

4 For her birthday, we bought my grandma her favourite flowers: daffodils, tulips and roses.

Prefixes and suffixes (page 30)

1 anti

2 joyfulness; direction, directness; builder, building

3 dis

4 autograph; subaqua; aquamarine

5 Accept any word ending in -ness, e.g. plainness; sadness.

Prefixes (page 31)

1 Accept sentences that use these words appropriately:

disappointment; disarm; disconnect; discourage; dishonourable.
The sentences must be correctly punctuated.

2 a) disclose; b) discontented; c) detained; d) destruction; e) desolate

3 a) inexcusable
 b) impertinent
 c) irreverent
 d) imperfect
 e) illegal
 f) illogical
 g) impossible
 h) indirect

Suffixes: -tion, -ssion, -cian (page 32)

1 2 marks - all correct
 1 mark - 7 correct words or more
 Ends in d, de or se:

apprehend	apprehension
persuade	persuasion
ascend	ascension
decide	decision
extend	extension
confuse	confusion

Ends in c or cs:

politic	politician
electric	electrician

Ends in ss or mit:

permit	permission
express	expression
possess	possession

Ends in another way:

divert	diversion
exhibit	exhibition
inject	injection

2 a) repetition; b) adaptation; c) expulsion; d) evolution

Suffixes: -ous, -tious, -cious (page 33)

1
boisterous	lively
callous	hard-hearted
carnivorous	meat-eating
conscious	awake
cautious	careful
momentous	important
courteous	well-mannered

2 4 marks
Accept sentences that use these words appropriately: infectious; religious; notorious; outrageous.
The sentences must be correctly punctuated.

3 furious; various; glorious; studious; injurious

Suffixes: -able, -ably, -ible, -ibly (page 34)

1 a) plausible; b) unreachable;
c) unintelligible; d) edible;
e) irreversible

2 2 marks - all correct
1 mark - 3 correct
unnoticeable; probably;
unbelievable; flexible

3 6 marks
classifiable; identifiable; reliable;
enviable; pitiable. Accept sentences
that use these words appropriately.

Suffixes: -ant, -ance, -ancy, -ent, -ence, -ency (page 35)

1 preference   choice
advance   go forwards
magnificent   wonderful
conference   meeting
existence   life
incompetence   failure

2 absent; diligently; performance;
audience; interference; persistently

3 circle: transparent; acquaintance;
resistance; perseverance; vigilant;
insignificant

Words with ie, ei, eigh, ey, ay (page 36)

1 a) achievement; b) convenient;
c) courier; d) niece; e) fiercely

2 2 marks - all correct
1 mark - 7 correct or more
ei words:
ceiling
protein
counterfeit
deceitful
Einstein
foreigner
height
heiress
ie words:
alien
hygienic

relieve
field

3 a) heiress; b) counterfeit; c) Einstein;
d) hygienic; e) foreigner

Words with ough (page 37)

1 a) enough; b) boughs; c) hiccoughs;
d) wrought; e) afterthought;
f) drought

2 roughness/est/en; thoroughness;
toughness/est/en; thoughtfulness

3 brougham   a type of horse-
drawn carriage
thoroughfare   a roadway
doughty   hardy, brave
furlough   a period of leave
for a soldier
slough off   get rid of
thoroughbred   a type of racehorse

Word endings: al, el, il, le (page 38)

1 anvil   a blacksmith's tool
uncivil   impolite
abnormal   unusual
cardinal   a high-status job in the
church
admiral   an officer in the navy
satchel   a type of bag

2 fossil; aerial; applicable; coastal;
presidential; professional;
icicle; sentimental; carousel;
mythical; barrel; terrible; parallel;
archaeological; squirrel

3 audible; criminal; peril; carousel

Silent letters (page 39)

1 circle: a) handkerchief; b) scene;
c) scissors; d) hymn; e) crumb;
f) fascinate; g) campaign; h) solemn;
i) guilt

2 a) whistle; b) guess; c) gnome;
d) tomb; e) crescent; f) design;
g) sandwich; h) listen; i) knowledge;
j) rogue

3 5 marks
Accept sentences that make sense.
The sentences must be correctly
punctuated.

Homophones (page 40)

1 a) board; b) desert; c) accept;
d) queue; e) stationary

2 loan   lone
maid   made
bawled   bald/balled
bear   bare
alter   altar
seam   seem
sighed   side
sole   soul

3 a) maize; b) mist; c) seize; d) sort;
e) shake

Synonyms and antonyms (page 41)

1 tick: agree

2 wandering   direct
aggressive   pacifying
achieve   abandon
durable   weak

3 tick: confirm

4 tick: old-fashioned

5 comply   agree
coerce   persuade
corrupt   destroy
collate   organise

Word families (page 42)

1 tick: correspondent;
correspondence

2 deliver

3 improved/improvement/improvable

4 tick: hide

5 Accept an answer that uses 'curve'
as a noun and makes sense, e.g.
I drew a curve on my diagram.
The sentence must be correctly
punctuated.

6 Accept an answer that uses 'curve'
as a verb and makes sense, e.g. The
road curved around the hillside.
The sentence must be correctly
punctuated.